"Who are the boxes from?" Doc asks.

"I'll give you a hint," Mum says. "She travels all over the world and she loves you a whole lot."

"GRANDMA!" Doc and Donny shout.

It looks like Grandma's in Hawaii!

She sent Donny a ukulele.

"How does this sound?" Donny asks as he strums the strings.

Doc opens her parcel.

"Oh, wow!" she says. "A Hawaiian hula dancer! She's beautiful."

Mum tells Doc that her new doll will dance to Hawaiian music.

Doc can't wait to see that!

She takes the doll to the clinic to show her friends.
Doc's stethoscope glows and all her toys come to life.
"Guys, look what my grandma sent!" calls Doc.

"The sunniest Hawaiian greetings to everybody!" the doll says cheerfully. "My name is Leilani. *Aloha!*"

"Welcome to sunny Hawaii!" Leilani continues.

Then she takes a look around the clinic.

"*E kala mai ia'u!* Excuse me!" she says. "Where am I?"

"You're a long way from Hawaii," Hallie tells her. "But we're glad you're here!"

"Oh, no!" Leilani cries. "I don't want to wave *aloha* to my beautiful islands. I'll miss them so much!"

Chilly wants to know what Hawaii is like.

"Are there snowmen, like me?" he asks.

"No snowmen!" Leilani replies. "Most of the time
it's sunny and warm."

"We Hawaiians love swimming and surfing," she adds.

"Who doesn't?" laughs Surfer Girl as she surfs by.

Leilani starts to sway her hips, hands and shoulders.

"The thing I'll miss the most is dancing the hula!" she says sadly.

"When I dance, I am the islands! Oh, I miss Hawaii so much!"

"We have to do something," Lambie whispers to Doc.
Doc agrees.

Then Doc has a great idea.

She can throw a *luau* for Leilani.

It's a big party with Hawaiian food and music.

The toys get busy.

Hallie and Chilly hang
garlands of flowers.

Stuffy and Lambie
make grass skirts.

Sir Kirby, Hermie, Bronty
and Niles, the crane, work
together to make a palm tree.

*"Mahalo,* Doc!" Leilani cries. "Thank you!"

The clinic looks just like her home.

Now it's hula time!

"When I dance the hula, I tell stories with every move of my hips, my hands and my shoulders," Leilani explains. "Try it!"

Doc and all the toys start to sway to the music.

"My hippo hips were meant to hula!" Hallie shouts.

Leilani's hula starts to slow down.

It gets slower and slower and then it stops.

"Oh, no! This is *not* the hula!" Leilani cries.

Leilani didn't mean to stop, but she can't dance another step.

"Doc, what's wrong with Leilani?" Stuffy wonders.

"I'm not sure," Doc replies. "But I'm going to find out."

It's time for Leilani's check-up.

Doc checks Leilani's ears and eyes.

Then she listens to her heartbeat.

"Leilani, everything looks like it should be working," Doc says. "Can you show me your hula again?"

"I just can't!" cries Leilani. "I'm too tired to do the moves!"

Hallie notices that Leilani looks tired.
Doc agrees that her energy seems low.

Doc has a diagnosis.

"Leilani, you have a case of No-hula-tosis," she says.

"It's when you don't have enough energy to dance."

Doc knows what's wrong with Leilani, but now she
needs to find out why.
She flips through the Big Book of Boo-Boos.

Ricardo had a case of
No-*vroom-vroom*-atosis
because his batteries were low.
Leilani doesn't have batteries,
so that can't be the problem.

Melinda Mermaid had
Stuck-winder-upperitis.
Leilani doesn't have
a windup key, so that can't
be the problem either!

Doc is stumped.

"Leilani, I'm not sure *how* you get energy!" she admits.

"I wish I knew!" Leilani says. "In Hawaii, I sat in a sunny
toy store window. As long as the bright Hawaiian sun
was out, I'd hula from sunrise to sundown!"

Now Doc has the clue she needs.
She carries Leilani to the window and holds her towards
a ray of sun. Hawaiian music begins to play.

"Happy heaps of hippos!" Hallie shouts.
"When the sun shines on that glass, that little yellow
light glows!"

"You get your energy from the sun!" Doc tells Leilani.
"This little solar panel makes electricity by using light
from the sun."

Doc tells her toys that it's time to move the party outside.
"Everybody needs to go outside and play in the sun
sometimes," Lambie says.

The toys move the *luau* decorations to Doc's sunny garden.

Doc sets Leilani on the water table.

*"Aloha!"* Surfer Girl calls. "Did Doc help?"

*"Aloha!"* Leilani calls back. "I hope so."

A ray of sunlight hits Leilani.
Then another ... and another ... and then....

It's hula time!

"*Mahalo nui loa*, Doc!" Leilani says gratefully. "That means 'Thank you very much'. As long as I can hula dance, I'll always have Hawaii with me!"

The End

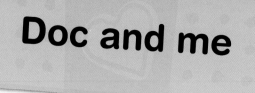

# Doc and me

This is Doc McStuffins.
Can you wave
hello to her?

Hello, Doc!

Doc is six years old and she
has a special secret....
Her magic stethoscope can
bring toys to life!

Doc can't wait to find out all about you.
Will you answer her questions?

What's your name?

TIFFANY

How old are you?

6

Stick in a picture of yourself!

# Dream job

Doc's dream job is to look after toys and make them better. She loves being a toy doctor!

What is your dream job?
Would you like to be a firefighter,
an astronaut or a pirate?

In the circle below, draw a picture
of you doing your dream job!

# Little friends

Doc's toys are her very best friends. They all take care of each other!

Name: Lambie
Kind of toy: Stuffed lamb
Says: 'Do you need a cuddle?'

Name: Stuffy
Kind of toy: Stuffed dragon
Says: 'I totally knew that.'

Name: Hallie
Kind of toy: Stuffed hippo
Says: 'Happier than a hippo!'

Name: Chilly
Kind of toy: Stuffed snowman
Says: 'I can't feel my legs!'

Do you have any teddies or stuffed animals?
Which one is the most cuddly?

Draw or stick in a picture of your favourite toy.

My favourite toy is called

mr bEAr.

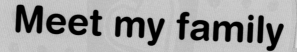

# Meet my family

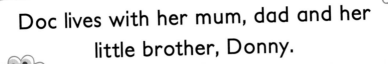

Doc lives with her mum, dad and her little brother, Donny.

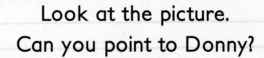

Look at the picture.
Can you point to Donny?

Doc would love to meet your family!

Draw or stick in a picture of your family.

# A huggy home

This is the house where Doc lives with her family.

Look at the picture.
Can you circle the chimney?

Now Doc would like to see where you live!
Draw or stick in a picture of your home here.

# Too many tools!

It's no wonder Doc's medical bag is feeling heavy –
she accidentally packed two of each tool!
Draw lines to join the tools that match.

# Design a bag

Doc always keeps her medical bag handy.
Decorate your own bag below,
then add lots of colour!

# The doc is in!

Doc's clinic is in a playhouse in her garden.
Look at the picture. Can you point to the door?

What colour is it?

Doc would like a new picture for her waiting room wall. Will you draw one for her below? You can draw a picture of anything you like!

# On the go

Doc and her dad have made a clinic on wheels, so that Doc can help toys wherever she goes! Look at the picture. Where is Doc today?

Pretend you have your own mobile doctor's clinic.
Draw circles around the things you would
choose to carry in it.

# A colourful coat

Doc always wears a white coat. What colour coat would you choose? Add your favourite colour!

# It's magic!

Can you remember what Doc's stethoscope does when she puts it on? Draw your own stethoscope and add some stars to make it magical!

# A colourful kit

All Doc's medical tools are pink and purple.
For your doctor's kit, make these tools
your favourite colours!

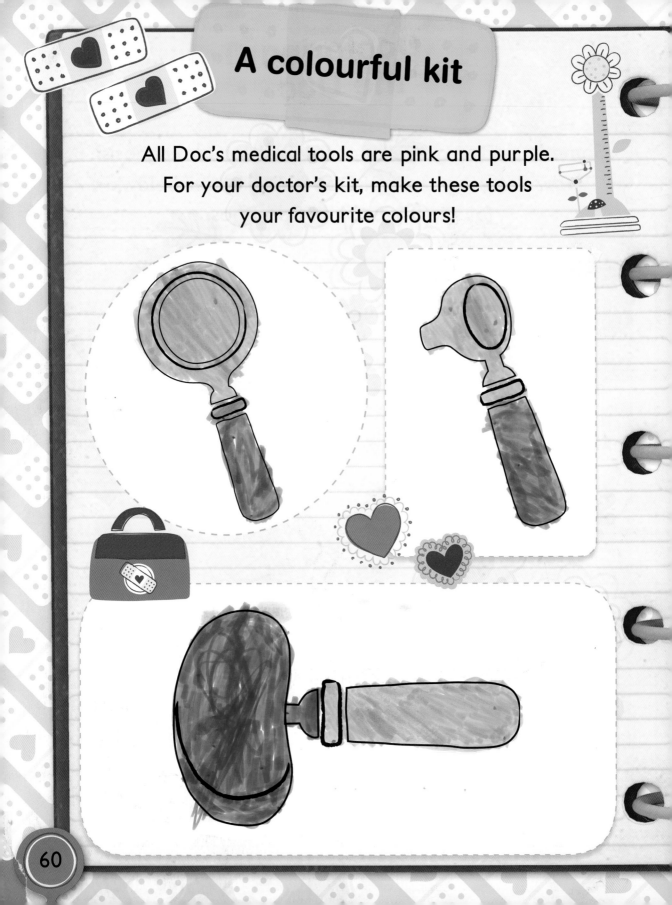